Salt in our Blood

Salt in our Blood

an anthology of west coast moments

compiled and edited by Joanna Streetly

ISBN 0-9730989-0-2

Published by Aquila Instincts Creative Services
Box 535, Tofino,
B.C. V0R 2Z0
Canada

First Printing, 2002

Editing by Joanna Streetly
Interior book design and typesetting by Jan Brubacher
Illustrations by Elizabeth Streetly
Cover Design by Jan Brubacher
Cover art by Signey Cohen
Cover photo taken circa 1914, courtesy of the Bert Drader collection

Printed and bound on 100 percent recycled paper in Victoria, BC

Table of Contents

Acknowledgements

"There's no place like Vargas." These are Marilyn Buckle's words and they are true. Neil and Marilyn's unique brand of westcoastness is inspiring! It is infectious. Their warm hospitality and wealth of stories have been invaluable to the creation of this book.

My mother, Elizabeth Streetly, overcame airmail, a ticking clock and the Tofino post office to illuminate the letters, while Jan Brubacher's computer wizardry made everything beautiful.

One glance at Signey Cohen's beautiful painting was all it took to find material for the cover. The Bert Drader photo is a welcome addition.

Technical and business details would have been worrisome without the help of Gerhard Aichelberger, Michael Mullin and Dorothy Baert.

Invaluable last-minute help from Jackie Windh and Janice Lore.

Thank-you to all these people. And to everyone who contributed a west coast moment. It's been inspiring!

Introduction

Life on the west coast of Vancouver Island is full of sur-
prises and unique challenges, most of which are caused by
the elements. I was reminded of this as I shovelled partially-
melted snow out of my boat one late-spring day, with a
plastic dustpan. This, I thought, as my sodden fingers froze,
is a truly west coast moment.

My mind immediately leaped to other "moments" in
my life here, like living on a 28-foot, partially-covered sports
fishing boat and raising seven puppies in the rainy season
(unavoidable circumstances); like jumping with near-hys-
terical joy on Long Beach because I had found my first ever
Japanese glass fishing float, which later floated away from
me; like being late for work because the fog was so thick.

When I thought of these moments collectively they
made up a colourful spectrum. The idea of soliciting and
collecting other people's "moments" was too good to pass
up. And because of their brevity, "moments" are well-suited
to a new genre of writing - the postcard story. Such stories
are brief and action packed, like a quick sketch, or snapshot.
Authenticity is the key. This collection's authors have used
it to great effect.

Everyone sees the west coast differently, but there is a thread of constancy, like a common language: the water, the weather, the forests, the beaches. We all experience the same environment, but in different ways. Even the mundane aspects of life can be shaped by the elements into something unusual.

Threaded through the wealth of stories is the voice of Neil Buckle. Neil's sons make up the fourth generation of his family to live on the west coast. To First Nations people, that is just the blink of an eye, but for Neil, combined with his flair for story-telling, it is time enough to have nurtured some compelling memories. His narrative serves as an historical counterpoint to the collected stories. His voice tells us the way things were on the west coast, in Neil's life, not too long ago.

This anthology records only a fraction of the infinite pool of west coast moments. Many voices are missing from this small book. Perhaps that just makes more for next time....

Prologue

It's evening and the fog hasn't lifted all day. We boat over to the Vargas Island Inn, moor the boat out in Mill Bay and crunch up the pebble beach to Neil and Marilyn's cabin. They are tucked into the corner of the bay, away from the manor where their guests are housed. They moved here in the seventies from their home, The Comber's Resort, on Long Beach. The government bought them out so that Long Beach could be "preserved for all time" and turned into a park.

We climb the steps to the cabin, under the overhanging branches of a hemlock tree. Through the glass doors, Florence Margaret barks us a black-Lab welcome.

Later, we sit comfortably, eating salmon, crab and freshly dug potatoes, our feet resting on the varnished planks of the cedar floor, our plates on varnished cedar tables, their doweled corners testament to Marilyn's flair for woodworking. The wood itself likely came from Neil's sawmill, where for years he has milled lumber brought to him by local salvagers.

Neil Buckle's grandfather, Francis Garrard, was the first lighthouse keeper at Lennard Island. He helped to construct the light. Neil grew up on the coast and is always full of stories. He has promised to tell me some of them, which is why we are here.

Marilyn is standing beneath a row of hanging kitchen utensils, taking bones out of a freshly barbecued salmon. Larry, who helps out at Vargas, is sitting in his corner chair, nursing a can of Blue and showing me a talking watch. It tells you the time, with a Chinese accent, every hour, from six a.m. to midnight. You can buy them at his store, a five minute walk through the rainforest from here.

Neil settles himself comfortably and the memories flow. I scribble notes, but can't keep up, so I press the red "record" button and let a machine preserve the words. You'll find Neil's narrative alternating with the other stories in this book.

# oastal Spring

Jade, olive, malachite, viridian, emerald, lime, sea-glass . . . There are not enough words for the hues of green in a coastal forest. After months of winter rain, plants are flush with water, cells fully plumbed. Days lengthen, soil steams, decay hastens, releasing new fragrance, a humousy funk, the earthy fecundity of spring. Alchemy plays out beneath the soil and in the burgeoning tips of plants. Cells rearrange, roots stretch, leaves clutch one another in a tightly bound coil; one last embrace before they break out of a bud, unfurl their leaves and tilt them skyward.

Salmonberry flowers let loose their petals and flash their shocking pink skirts, exhibiting their wares with

1

a come-hither flag to rufous hummingbirds, ready for a fix of nectar after a long, lonely flight from Mexico. The flash of the males' shimmering red gorgets and their frenzied buzz as they zip from salmonberry to flowering red currant, in passionate pursuit of sweetness and females, is the coast's first dance of spring fever.

The ditches and muddy margins of forest paths are filled with phalluses. Brilliant canary cloaks of skunk cabbages enfold their flower-covered columnar spathes, a heady scent to lure beetles and flies, which wallow in the nectar and dust themselves with pollen. Putrid or perfume, it is the unmistakable aroma of a coastal spring.

Coastal people are affected by this shift in seasons, too. We lift our faces to the sun, expose our arms, our heads, our feet. Show a little skin. It's getting hot under all that rubber.

Adrienne Mason

Millions of Mice

"About 1958 there was a huge outbreak of mice at Long Beach. Thousands and thousands of them. There was a gravel road and you could actually see the crushed mice all over the road. The mice were everywhere, on the logs, in the forest - everywhere. Just tens of thousands of them - millions, even. There they were, running around, and we were sleeping up in the loft, with no insulation in the roof. The mice would be running around over our faces, while we were sleeping."

"One day during that time, our neighbour came along and wanted us to go with him to the wreck of the *Carelmapu*. That was a Chilean freighter that had gone down at Radar Beach. So we went along with him to salvage dead-eyes. When we got back up to the top of the hill we were all sweaty and we crawled into one of those cement buildings and got very cold. Then, when we came back to our place at Comber's, some people had got a car stuck in the surf, so we went wading out to help them."

"I started coughing that night, really badly. I didn't have a cold, or anything. I just started hacking and coughing. Cough, cough, cough. And by morning I was coughing up blood! I could hardly move."

"Mum said: 'We've got to take you to the hospital.' So off we went and Dr Janz and his wife, who was also a doctor, told me I'd got pneumonia. When I look back, I think it was that disease, hantavirus, that you get from mice, but back then, in 1958, they didn't know about hantavirus. They gave me penicillin and I'd never had that before, so - boom! - I was instantly healthy."

"Shortly after that epidemic, we had mink living in our house. They set up underneath our boiler and they were eating mice. They were a great help."

a-aat

Pacific tree frogs feature in the mythology and artwork of coastal First Nations people who know them as wa-aat.

There is a construction site across from my house. From a puddle in a wheel rut I hear his incessant call: "Wa-aat! Wa-aat! Wa-aat!"

Perhaps he has a woman in his puddle with him and he is serenading her with amorous eyes. Or maybe he is calling, waiting, hoping that love will hop into his life.

I sit on my porch on cool April evenings. "Wa-aat! Wa-aat! Wa-aat!"

It goes on. It is too much! "What?" I call back. I must

see him, or them. These little voices belong to emerald jewels, so loudly heard yet seldom seen.

I hike across the street under a dusky violet sky. In dim light I squat beside the wheel rut, an inch of water in a puddle a couple of feet long. No frogs, but a lumpy mass of jelly the size of a twoonie. I scoop them out.

For ten days they sit on the kitchen windowsill. Are they even alive? Perhaps they have already dried out. Perhaps the water is too warm. Then, one morning, action! I peer in and three little black lines the size of hemlock needles rest on the bottom. Before my very eyes the entire mass wiggles and another tadpole shoots upward to freedom.

By noon I am the proud mother of 13 tiny frogs-to-be. Summer days are spent scooping algae out of ditches to feed my brood. I remember, when I was a child, my father making me pour my jar of tadpoles out. "When you are a grown-up and live in your own house, then you can have tadpoles."

I guess I am grown up now.

Wa-aat?

Jacqueline Windh

The Good Friday Tsunami

"It was 1964, Good Friday. My son, Andrew, had just been born and I came back to Comber's from the hospital quite late. I didn't go out celebrating, or anything. There were no warnings about a tsunami, but my neighbour up the hill heard about the Anchorage earthquake on the ten o'clock news."

"A rumbling roar woke me up. I got up and went outside to see what was happening, but there was no wind, or anything. The salal was completely still. Then I looked and saw that the water was right level with the bank and there were logs banging around in it. The roar was the noise of water pouring and pouring into the sand bank."

"'Oh for Christ's sake, it's a tidal wave!' I realized, because the water never came that high, normally. It was absolutely mesmerizing. These big spruce trees were snapping in two or three pieces and the logs were banging and clunking around. They caused a log jam that lasted for years and years. It went a good mile up Sandhill Creek."

"Then all of a sudden the water seemed to go. It just - left! And as it did so, the logs that were in the creek come tumbling down, end over end. These huge logs being tossed like match sticks and the water raging out towards the ocean. I was totally stunned."

The iss

He kissed me like a young, shy stranger: tenderly, with a degree of innocence. But he didn't fool me. His lips were deliciously skilled. I wanted more. I wanted that cool softness like air and water, a coolness that heated my body into a vibrating hum of tantric energy – a term these west coast people tend to over-use.

These *westcoasters*. (Sigh.)

He said we could do amazing healing work together by "funnelling our desire." What I wanted was for us to go whole-hog somewhere deep in the old growth forest. Why dam a river? Surely he would be into going with the flow.

9

In my fantasy, after staggering out of the bush, we would ravish each other in the shallow waters as the tide went out, and then roll around on the mudflat for hours, frightening the herons. An owl hooting . . . hands on skin . . . a raven croaking . . . his mouth on my belly . . . bald eagles calling to one another . . . the two of us coming together, our cries caressing the tree tops. At one with passion and the elements, biting and clawing like mating otters, while dragonflies darted and hovered around our bodies for a touch of the surreal.

Instead, I was kissed on the lips by some kind of magic charge, a candle glowing before my face, eyes involuntarily closed by the sheer force of Eros. Then he jumped into a boat and headed for the open ocean.

And when I went alone to the mudflat it was cold and clammy and chopstick-legged shore birds were piercing it with their long bills in search of small, slimy food. But this was all right. I could handle it. I empathized with the oystercatcher, all black, prying helpless limpets from rocks with a very red mouth.

Christine Lowther

The Second World War

"When we first moved to Comber's, there were certainly a lot of signs of the war. We used to go up to the airport and find all sorts of ammunition - grenades and everything. If the Japanese ever got to the airport, there was a switch you could throw from where we were at the Comber's and blow up all the runways and everything. There were tunnels under there, with dynamite in them."

"They had a pretty good arsenal. We were ploughing the field one time and we found a mortar bomb. There we were, tossing this thing back and forth."

"When the Japanese submarine was supposed to have fired on Estevan Light there was a black-out in Tofino. At the time there was a party at the

Wingens'. Somebody was passed out in one of the bedrooms with the light on. So there was this big bedroom light shining out over the harbour. The only light in the harbour. I guess everybody else got the news."

"But I think the bombing was just a fake, anyway. To frighten people. I heard that they callipered the size of the shell and it wasn't Japanese. It was US or Canadian."

Clayoquot Jays and Me

Cougars? Black Bears? Wolves? Real and imaginary, I stared them all down, that summer of '92 at Cypress Bay in Clayoquot Sound where I was homesteading. But the insane curiosity of the blue-backed Steller's Jays - birds without a modicum of humility or decorum - almost defeated me.

It was their fascination with my daily bath, out by the cedar and hemlock trees, that made me realize they were also a bunch of perverts.

Every time I approached the big blue plastic barrel, half-full of sun-warmed water, with towel and soap in hand, a few feathered scouts immediately set up the alarm. Come one! Come all! The show is about to begin! Soon the lower branches of the trees filled. And the audience seemed to swell daily. Fifty, seventy-five, a hundred or more little black heads, with beady black eyes that swivelled from side to side as they eye-balled all my movements prior to stepping into the barrel.

And they were silent the entire time I bathed. It was creepy. Really.

I started stashing rocks near the barrel. Periodically, I would scatter them towards the tree branches to try to disperse my audience. They would flutter away briefly and then flutter right back to their front row seats.

It wasn't until the popcorn incident that I started fantasizing about a pellet gun.

What was I thinking the day I threw out some unpopped popcorn seeds? Off my front deck? The jays loved them. They landed on my deck demanding more. I beat a hasty retreat inside. Later, they accompanied me to the outhouse. They followed me to the beach, dogged every step I took. I was being stalked. Yes, a pellet gun.

I didn't buy the gun. I just stopped eating popcorn because the little monsters watched from the picture window and it got too cold to bathe outside. But I knew the struggle wasn't over. It had merely subsided for the season.

Betty Krawczyk

The Skiff Sinking

"The skiff's sunk twice - no - three times; well - two *real* sinkings. We had to rescue it off the bottom once when Dave and Una were here and then again this last time. When I got up that morning I saw the thing wallowing and thought, 'Jeez, that looks *really* low in the water.' And by the time I was dressed, it was really low in the water - there was just the bow sticking up!"

"I never worry about the herring skiff itself. I worry about the motor. Last time, my worry was: 'Am I going to get to it and get organized in time, before it sinks completely and takes the damn buoy and everything under with it? And then, how do I tow it in, or do anything with it when it's down there on the bottom?'

"So I was out there with the little rowboat, sawing away on the damn tie-up line because it was so tight to the herring skiff. It was three-quarter inch rope and I had a tiny little knife. The surge was bashing me around and I was thinking, 'Aw shoot, I'm going to get caught and pinched here.'

15

"Prior to that I'd put a line on the skiff, all the way to shore. Finally I did get the rope cut off and then, once I got it loose, I backed the skidder down and just slowly winched it ashore. It was underwater all the time and I was wondering: 'Where is the goddamn thing?'

"Derek had come over and asked, 'Is it right side up or upside down?' but I didn't even know. I slowly dragged it up, but the motor fell off and got totally wrecked because it just bashed around in the surge. It's history now."

ater Damage

After being in charge of a hotel for three years the thought of running a first-rate Bamfield resort in the owner's absence did not frighten me in the least. Cheerfully, and with confidence, I greeted the guests on the east side of the inlet and we boated over to the resort dock. I loaded their luggage into the wagon attached to the all-terrain vehicle, while the family headed up the hill in front of me, to the cabins.

The ramp from the main part of the dock to solid ground is narrow, but the all-terrain vehicle does fit on it. The route has been done often and I had even done it myself, a couple of times.

I gave the bike a bit of gas to get over the lip from dock to ramp, but the engine was more responsive than I expected it to be and I went tearing onto the ramp. Unfortunately, brake action did nothing and I found myself ploughing headfirst through the railing and into the cold March ocean. The machine sank fast underneath me as I cursed, all too loudly, luggage and food floating all around me. Recent Coast Guard Auxiliary training slipped my mind as I grabbed frantically, trying to save every last item from water damage.

Everything was rescued, although with some damage done, but thankfully the guests were understanding. The all-terrain vehicle was dragged across the inlet to get fixed. Eventually, even my guilt dissipated. Apparently, accidents like this do happen in Bamfield, so I don't feel like such a newcomer to the rugged west coast anymore.

Karen Odenwald

The Skiff Sinking - Again

"When we had that El Niño year, the storms were horrendous. We'd been warned, so I had the skiff well prepared and every time I went out to it, I'd check the pumps and make sure things were working right. You could actually hear it from here: the BOOM! as the skiff was going up on the wave, then BOOM! as it was coming down again. The waves lifted the bow way up. You could hear it even above the screeching wind and everything else."

"One time, after we'd been down at Dave and Una's, the anchor came unhooked and the boat drifted in. All that pounding on the rocks ground a hole in the gas tanks, so there was gas in the boat and it was full of water."

"We came home from their place at two in the morning and there was the herring skiff sitting sideways on the rocks. I ended up having to go and get the skidder. But it was night and the skidder's got no lights or anything. So I had to drive that darn thing in the dark, backing it around in the bush before I could pull the boat up on the beach."

"After that, I had to get a siphon hose and siphon the tanks, because there was about 45 gallons of gas in the darn thing. Actually that's probably an exaggeration, there was probably only about thirty gallons or whatever. . . ."

ombrio

Sombrío adj. shady, gloomy. Tenía un aspecto muy sombrío. She had a very gloomy appearance.
Sombrio Beach n. a piece of mostly rocky beach on the southwest coast of Vancouver Island; part of the provincial park system.

Before it was a park, it was our home. Shelters made of driftwood and plastic wrapped in the arms of trees. Sombrío in the Spanish sense - fog and mist and rain. Winter winds strong enough to turn houses into hammocks. Summer sun bright and temperate. Naked walks the length of the beach collecting smooth stones. Big ones. Flattened by unrelenting waves. To heat the sauna. Also made of driftwood and plastic. Right by the river that feeds into the ocean. The best sweats I ever had in my life. Later we'd gather mussels for dinner. Always made an offering first, the spirits ever present. And vocal. Bossy, even. One time I went into town for supplies, forgot to ask if George, who lived way at the other end of the beach by himself, needed anything. When I returned, a cougar had slashed the door to my hut. A small slash. Just a reminder. We were supposed to watch out for each other. It was like that on the beach. Messages everywhere if you cared to see them.

Now it's a park. Huts all gone. No trace of any sauna. Before Sombrio was my home, it was somebody else's. The First Nations. We were the second. Or maybe the third. Or fourth. And so on. Back through time. And forward together. The only way really.

Joanne Bealy

West Coast Smog

"When I was working for Millstream one summer, we burned slash at Lost Shoe Creek. We'd logged there all summer, about 300 acres or more. Hans Larsen was the foreman then and he got orders, because it was supposed to be foggy at night, that it was safe to burn the slash."

"What you have to do, burning slash, is go out with a propane torch. They had it all sort-of figured and they sent the guys along the road first to torch all the really heavy slash there. That started the fire in the centre which would pull the air in from the sides. Then the crew going around the edge of the forest would torch in behind, so supposedly it'd burn into the centre, not into the forest. Which it did."

"I've never seen a fire like that, in my whole life!"

"I was working further up and when I came back with the crummy, the fire was going full bore.

It was a hot day in August; a super-hot day. You could see the vapours coming off the ground about 20 feet - all these clear vapours - and then they would ignite in a blue flame. The flames started twirling around like a tornado and made a screech like a jet plane taking off. It was an unimaginable fire."

"At one point, they were worried that some of the crew were still out there, so Hans went dashing off with a pickup truck - through all those flames! - and we thought, 'Oh God, his gas tank's going to explode and he'll be done for!'

"They got a real good burn. But, by next morning the fog had drifted in from the ocean and mixed with all the smoke. I've never seen fog like it. You couldn't see a car without headlights on, until it was about ten feet away. The crummy driver couldn't see the edge of the road, so somebody would have to be on the running boards or walking alongside to give directions. I said, 'How are we going to log, we can't even see?' So we all went home."

og Ferries

It was the perfect lesson in advanced sea kayaking. I was sitting with a group of students behind a rock, in the back eddy. They were visibly nervous - the current was whipping by and we were shrouded in a thick fog. We were there to practice the tricky technique of ferry gliding: crossing a channel by angling into the current, so that rather than being swept downstream, or worse yet, having to slog upstream, the kayak side-slips across the current.

Suddenly, a figure in a tiny dinghy materialized out of the mist. Angling steadily into the strong current, he executed a flawless ferry glide straight towards us. As the bow crossed the eddy line, the boat turned sharply and began heading upstream towards the rock. Without breaking rhythm, the boat passed right by my flabbergasted group. Laser Dave nodded to me as he rowed; a routine morning commute to work in Tofino.

Reaching the top of the eddy, his wee boat peeled out into the rip current and ferry-glided off into the fog. The words on the back of his boat read *Zig-Zag, Finito*. Turning to the group after watching this stellar demonstration of the advanced skills we were about to learn, I asked, "And are there any questions?"

Dan Lewis

West Coast Smog

Marilyn starts the fire in the woodstove with a good squirt from the propane blow torch. She's lived these stories too. She's been listening to most of them and occasionally augmenting. The fog affected her guests at Comber's Resort.

"We'd just started the Comber's Resort," she explains, "and we had guests, of course, a few guests, not very many, mind you, but oh, it was such a disappointment! The guests would come to the beach - to Comber's and Long Beach - but they could not see the beach. They couldn't see it all day. Two weeks went by and they still couldn't see the beach. They'd come from the Okanagan and they'd made reservations for two weeks, but the whole time they were there, until the last day, the fog never lifted and they never saw the beach. They never saw the ocean. That's the very truth."

ortow

Sliding out of the quiet foggy rain,
the purposeful little tug finds its exact place,
gently caresses the float, then backing off with a snort,
lunges deliberately and the log is in its proper space.

A line is skillfully looped and cinched.
The freshly-placed log securely tied.
Ladies discreetly peek through home-canning steamed
windows,
whose escape from the greyness will not be denied.

Louis Druehl

Punch And Mabel, Clydesdales On Long Beach

"There were two Clydesdales at Long Beach. Nellie Webb had one. The Webbs used to own the original Wickaninnish Lodge. Nellie had Punch, who was a male Clydesdale and she used him for getting firewood for their big cook stove."

"She had a saw called Wee MacGregor, which was one of the first power saws, but it worked like this [back and forth] with a motor. So she'd drag that thing along the beach on a sled, with the horse. She would set it up on a log on the beach and just start sawing. You could start the thing and it would just chug-chug-chug. You could be splitting blocks to the side as it went. Then it would drop through and hit a switch and shut itself off. You'd drag it over one block and start it up again. Nellie had the horse and buggy for that and she did that mostly through the winter. Then the horse was set free to roam around and graze throughout the summer."

"Nellie used to use Punch for beachcombing glass balls, too, so she had a terrible advantage over us, because when the creek was really high we couldn't even go through it without getting swept away, but the horse would just plunge into the creek and tow this wagon with huge wheels on it. And she'd load up glass balls and bark and everything else and fill the wagon. She had a huge advantage with this damn horse, because he never rusted like our jeeps."

"We used to shake our fist at Nellie Webb, when she came charging across the creek with Punch and the wagon."

Landbound

Four years ago I came to Ucluelet fresh from a life of sailing and adventure and tropical sea breezes. I came to Ucluelet and started to garden. And how I have embraced this new arrangement! Even, perhaps especially, when late-winter southeasters rattle the windows and shake the hemlock in the yard and throttle my tender new bedding plants.

My transition to gardener and land owner has not been all smooth sailing, however. Like now, on a spring morning, as I stand in my yard and stop my digging. Turning, I can see the inlet, a slight ruffle of wind on the water. A perfect sailing day. My rubber-booted foot (I haven't needed to change footwear at least) rests on the shovel and - eyes closed - I taste the salt air of other places and wonder what I am doing, not only landbound, but dirtbound. On days after a blow I can hear the surf pounding Ucluelet's other shore, where the next landfall, depending on your bearing, is Japan, Hawaii or Tonga.

When the fog's tendrils creep into my yard, I listen to the moan of the foghorn and wonder what it is I have taken refuge from in this safe harbour.

Sylvia Harron

Punch And Mabel,
Clydesdales On Long Beach

"Up the highway from us, Tommy MacDonald, the cougar hunter, had a Clydesdale, too. She was called Mabel. She was trained to pull power poles out of the bush because he had the contract to supply all the power poles for the power lines between Tofino and Ucluelet. And so he'd cut down hundreds and hundreds of poles and have this horse drag them out. Then he'd load them on trucks, with an old jury-rigged loader."

"But Mabel and Punch were both let loose through the summer and they'd come to our place at the Comber's. They kept the grass cropped down just perfectly and then they'd roam off to the sand dunes and graze there. From there, they'd go back up to Lovekin's meadow and then on to

Schooner Cove and Greenpoint. They were smart enough to realize that the time to move from one place to another was in the evenings, right at sunset, because the flies and everything would bug them so badly. So you'd see them both plodding along in the surf. The surf was good for their feet, I guess, and they knew it."

"It was a neat sight: sunset on Long Beach and these two huge horses plodding along through the surf."

eron feather island

to journey, solo by canoe, I need
high tide to float me out
of the sandal-sucking mudflats.
time of departure must depend
on the pull of the moon.

before leaving from the shore
I anticipate the wind
and pick up the largest rock
heedless of the homeless crabs
scurrying for safety.

the weight of worry on my shoulders
is lightened by a ballast,
my heavy rock companion sits
solid in the bow
of the faded yellow Clipper.

with ease I slice the surface
in the shallow see-through waters
where the sea has less resistance
to my pulling of the paddle
in a meditative rhythm.

glare of the sun, fear of the wind
makes me paddle even faster
to my chosen destination
almost within sight
muscles pumped with memory give me fuel.

shades of jade and pewter gray
deeper now, the choppy ocean
makes me hold my shallow breath
out of respect for its great power
cycle of life, silence of death.

I laugh out loud to see the island
as if my land-locked time
could cause it such rejection
that it would disappear
so infrequent are my visits.

gently, the Clipper scrapes the beach
the shore embraces me, a scene
a camera could not capture
for this is not a place
that a postcard could do justice.

I relax and comb the grasses, finding
plumes of great blue herons
discarded after breeding
no longer needed for their fancies
but coveted by humans.

on the stern of the canoe
scolding sound of small waves lapping
puts me in perspective
just a two-legged trespasser
dependent on a floating vessel.

still, I attempt to claim this place
by giving it a name while taking
feathers as reminders
of the energy in the sound, I will return
for the island
has its haunting hold on me.

J. McDougall

Punch And Mabel,
Clydesdales On Long Beach

"One time my brother was working with Warren Moreas for Hydro. They were putting in a power line to the Baxter's place, which is just south of Greenpoint. There was no road in there, so they had to drag the poles in."

"Hydro hired Mabel the horse. And they needed some extra help that day, so they hired me as well. We hitched up Mabel, but we didn't know a thing about horses. The horse knew a hell of a lot more than we did!"

"She would come up to where the pole was and turn around. Her rigging was three log-dogs on a chain and we'd drive the dogs in, all on the tip of the pole. Then one of us would tell her what to do - giddy-up, or whatever - and she'd start plodding along through all the roots and mud and everything else. There was a kink in the trail where there were some stumps, and the poles would get hung up. Mabel would just plod along and if the pole got hung up, she'd back up and try to pull it sideways and get it away from the hang-up. She'd try two or three times and then just turn around and look at you, as if to say, 'Come on you dummies, do something!'

"So we'd pry it over and say giddy-up and she'd plod along and away it would go. She seemed to know where to stop without being told. There'd be a hole dug to set the pole in and she would pull until the butt end was right near the hole and then stop."

"She seemed to know a whole lot more than we did! I thought, 'Good Lord, this horse is doing the whole damn thing!' We did nothing! It was a piece of cake."

The ungry Man

Wind was strong from the west, so the canoe rocked as the hungry man tied the Lucky Lure with ten-pound test. It was a high-tech lure - a buzz bomb with a high pitch, a dog whistle for fishes, not a lucky lure for them: technical weaponry.

The swell and the wind wanted to chase him onto the rocks, but somehow he knew he was at the spot. He saw the future: saw himself catch food right here, a minute from now, soon.

Put down paddle. Pick up pole. Flick with the wind. Watch lure fly and plop into sparkly water, tiny splash. Then pause. Breathe.

Jerk!

He started laughing. Laughing, he cranked on the reel, slacking off when it felt tight, keeping the tip up, yes; reeling it steadily, being calm, of course, and wise too.

The salmon broke the water shimmering, drops splashing off its spine, then dove, disappearing, gliding away on a run, towing the canoe and the hungry man too on one last erratic journey.

The fish jumped. And it spun in the air and dove again, this time down, down, line unreeling and stopped.

The line floated atop the water and he really reeled. He reeled the fish right up next to the canoe and reached for the line's end where the fish swirled, did a slow spin, silver, shiny.

As he pulled the salmon out of its home it thrashed and in the bottom of the canoe it flopped and flopped as it looked at him with yellow-green eyes, stared at him actually, assessing him, gills panting, until the hungry man took a deep breath and brought the paddle down hard on the salmon's brow and killed it.

It still watched him.

He wasn't hungry now.

Frank Harper

41

Punch And Mabel, Clydesdales On Long Beach

"When we were installing the poles, the foreman for the Hydro was a skinny little guy and he was wearing these big leather work boots. He said, 'This damn horse isn't working hard enough. I've worked with these horses before and I'm not impressed with the way she's working.'

"And so he grabbed Mabel by the bit in her mouth and started pulling on her and everything. Well, she got pissed off and she just tossed her head and - whing! - he went flying, over twenty feet into the bush: clunk, bang, crunch. He was bouncing off little saplings and everything. Then he crashed into the mud and the water. He got up and was pretty embarrassed by this time."

"He said 'Well, I think you guys are doing okay, I think I'll go now.'

"It was just amazing how smart that horse was!"

No Nonsense On The Water

To live year-round on a floathouse in the wilderness, you have to be tough and resourceful. Rather like a single mother.

Standing erect in her speeding boat, nearly-white dreadlocks streaming out comet-like behind her, small child in a well-worn lifejacket on the floor in front of her, Maddie was an impressive sight. She worked on several oyster farms, with the rough hands and biceps to prove it, and was renovating a floathouse.

The first time she and her three-year-old boy came to visit her nearest neighbour - me - I picked a cucumber from the vine in my floating greenhouse and gave it to them for their dinner. As Maddie talked, gesticulating with the cucumber - mainly about the renovation, mixed up with men and sex - her son fidgeted, trying to get our attention (not an easy task considering the subject matter).

"My next priority is to build a bed."

I was impressed, having just bought a bed from a friend. It would never have occurred to me to make one.

Maddie began taking bites out of the cucumber.

"Men my age in this town are scared of me."

I could see why. She was a no-nonsense, hard-working, hard-partying twenty-three-year old. On Saturday nights, her child went to his Dad's, and Maddie stalked the town in a big leather jacket, which she would remove before hitting the Legion dance floor to reveal a taut, tattooed, stretchmarked midriff.

"I'm fine for three weeks out of the month," she continued, mouth full, "it's just that other week. Problem is, I couldn't teach a guy to float out here in the winter. I won't be some bushboy's wetnurse!"

Soon, the cuke was gone. Maddie turned to her kid and said, "Come on, Zeus. Let's go home and make supper. I'm starving."

Christine Lowther

Cougars

"We did see cougars around Vargas when we first moved here. It wasn't actually a pleasant experience. It was when we'd just started the A-frame and I'd cleared a little bit of land up towards where the manor is now. Well, we'd found a wild cat, and called it Snowball, so our son, Chris, who was about three years old, knew what cats were."

"I was up around the manor cutting poles and what-not to make an outhouse and working all day with the power saw. Marilyn had Chris and they were over at the old foundation, clearing up the rubble from the previous house - putzing away there. We had a little bit of a garden happening there, too."

"Just before lunch Chris said to Marilyn, 'Whose 'nother cat Mummy? Whose 'nother cat?'

"So Marilyn asked him where he'd seen the cat,

because she was thinking it might be a cougar. But she never mentioned anything to me because she thought I'd pooh-pooh the idea and think she was paranoid. Just before we were going to leave for the day, I was going to trim off the poles that I'd brought down and I looked up and saw something move up in the bush. It was only 50 feet away, maybe. I thought: 'A deer? Oh no, for Chrissakes, it's a cougar!'

"That's what Christopher had seen. And it was big, menacing-looking beast. If Marilyn hadn't been gardening right by there, it would have gone for Chris. It was a young healthy male and they can be the most troublesome, because they almost feel invincible, really."

"He slowly turned around while he was watching me and slunk off into the bush, but he wasn't in any hurry at all. I had the power saw, which I knew would start immediately, first pull, and I thought, 'If you want to have it out, well, I've got a weapon too!'

ild and Woolly

Sheba's fluffy white tail followed her round the far side of the boat. When her nose appeared at the stern, her quizzical expression seemed to say, "Yes, it's a boat, but what the hell is it doing here amongst all this cow shit and rusting farm machinery?"

"Is that dog part wolf?" asked the owner, standing dead still as Sheba gave him a sniff.

"Yes," replied Annie. "Now about the scuppers, did you say the boat was self-bailing?"

Annie had driven across the island with Lana, to see this boat.

"You don't really know a boat till you see it," she said as I squeezed into her pick-up cab. The two were dressed in their usual rubber boots, fleece pants, tatty raincoats and wool toques.

"On the phone this guy said, 'A girl? Driving a pick-up? Towing a trailer? Coming to see a boat? *This* I have to see.' So I thought it would be best to have a man around, just in case. . . ."

I did my duty as a man and kicked the boat with the toe of my running shoe. "It should float," I offered Annie.

She turned back to Clancy.

"So what's under the floor? Is it foam filled?"

"No, it's just a workboat from a fishing charter service up-island. She's not pretty, but she's strong. What do you need her for anyway?"

"Getting back and forth to town."

"You don't live in Tofino then?"

"No, and I'm getting sick of banging up Browning Passage in my Boston Whaler when there's a 30 knot southeaster blowing."

"You girls sure are wild and woolly."

Annie looked over both the boat and Clancy one more time. Plenty of dents, the steering system was gutted and the electrical would need to be redone. Not worth the effort in the end. She thanked him anyway and we piled in the pick-up for the drive home. As we sped up the island highway heading back for the west coast, Annie turned to Lana: "Wild and woolly? What the hell did he mean by that?"

Mike Laanela

Driving on Long Beach

"There were always old car wrecks on Long Beach. The worst was when people tried to drive from Comber's to Wickaninnish, because that section was always full of soft spots where the sand had built up and the tourists never knew how to drive on the beach. They'd go close to the rocky headlands where it was all gooey and soft."

"People used to drive on Chesterman's, too, but it was pretty hard to get stuck on Chesterman's because it was so hard-packed. The old chassis at Chesterman's, that appears in the sand now and then, is from a carbecue."

"Carbecues were when people were partying and then they would decide, well, we don't need this car any more and they would set fire to it."

"Marilyn and I used to race on the beach. Marilyn had an MJB and I just had a regular car with a V8 engine. She beat me, going 105 miles per hour on Long Beach! From Incinerator to Green Point."

"Neil didn't rev his up enough!" Marilyn smiles serenely.

"I couldn't compete!" Neil exclaims. "That thing of Marilyn's used to go up to 7000 rpm!"

"Oh!" says Marilyn, "Is that it? And here I was, always thinking, well, it's such a little thing, why does it go so fast? I thought Neil was just not trying hard enough to beat me."

behind The Dump

Late summer weekend . . . Gottagetoutta this tourist town!

We grab the rods and stop for fuel, pop-and-smokes . . . wait ten minutes to pay. Grrr.

Speed past Pacific Rim Resort (full), motorhomes, Esowista hitchhikers (both directions) . . . sad little dramas unfolding in the Long Beach parking lot.

Left at the dump. Lots of bear shit outside the new electric fence. I'd hoped the bears might get angry - Organize Themselves, ya know? - but they just looked resigned . . . maybe a bit confused. Their noses pulling them one way and 5000 volts sending them back the other. From time to time we see a particularly sad fellow with a bright plastic ear tag . . . seems to know that one more misdemeanour and it's off to the big berry patch in the sky.

Past piles of garbage, old fridges, the firing range.

There are people back here, too. Speeding pick-ups carry mushroom pickers, wood thieves, guerilla pot growers and trout fishermen. They all seem to believe that if they avoid eye contact then you can't see them.

"That's the road where they found Clifford Olson. . . ."

"Uh-huh."

"Yeah, they say he had a couple of kids in the car with him. . . ."

Great.

We find our road. It's much worse this year. No logger's gonna fix this one until long after I'm dead. So we walk. Pickers have trashed our favourite chantarelle spot. Shit. Into the woods. Geez, the guy who named Devil's Club didn't need much of an imagination. Bend down. Stumble. Curse.

Finally, the river. Stop. Breathe. Silence.

. . .

A flash of silver.

Joy beckons.

Gear up.

Bill Morrison

52

Car Wrecks

"In my time at Comber's, I towed over 200 cars off the beach. One time, these guys had soaked the ignition and so they tried and tried to start it but they couldn't and the tide was coming in. They finally came up and said they needed a pull to get started."

"So I drove around by Incinerator Point in my old Ford car and hooked onto them. I pulled them and pulled them and pulled them and pulled them. I pulled them back and forth down the beach at - oh - 30 or 40 miles an hour, to try and start them."

"We did get it going in the end. It finally dried out just from the heat. They asked me what they owed me and I said 'Oh this will be 20 dollars,' or something like that and he said, 'Well, we don't have any money but we have a set of Snap-On Tools here. Can we leave them with you until we come and pay you tomorrow?'

"So I said, 'Oh! Oh! For sure!'

"The Snap-On Tools would have been super. They're the best of the mechanic's tools, like sockets and stuff. I was *really* hoping that he wouldn't come and pay me, but he did, unfortunately. "

"I never did make any money on the towing."

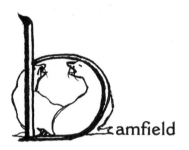amfield

The Bamfield I came to was filled with whiz-bang
and thank you gods-that-be, gracious matriarchs, laid-
back fisher folk and a whole cauldron of mild
sociopaths. A gentler time, when Len's machine-shop
wisdom prevailed and the Toms and Judys were, in
today's vernacular, cool dudes from far away, who
came escaping old-home evils or bringing those with
them. Today we see an invasion of aging baby
boomers, shaming Attila the Hun, we see the setting
sun and rising moon and rainbow people and wonder:
Are we missing the fun? And the land machines, the
barges, the honey wagon, summer folk, kayakers

peeking, snooping, probing every cranny and orifice and developers drooling over over-treed opportunities. Buy the land, clear the land, stir up the home-eating flying ants, little rectangles with littler boxes sell - BIG bucks. Winter comes and SUVs, tour buses and occasional mountain bikes (and no Volkswagon vans) escape to a sunnier place. Fewer regular folk now, but the rain feels clean and good on my face.

by Louis Druehl

The Korean War

"During the Korean War, in 1953 or so, they set up targets on the beach. They had a target on the island in Wreck Bay and they were bombing it for weeks with 500 pound bombs. The Mitchell bombers were doing that."

"Then they had targets in front of the sand dunes between our place and Wickaninnish, cheesecloth targets, about ten feet by ten feet, with a big bullseye. There were spotters on either end to stop people from wandering by when they were machine-gunning. The Mustang fighter planes would start about six in the morning. You'd hear: *Nnneeeeeowwwwww. D-d-d-d-d-d-d-d-d.* They also had a couple of barrels anchored in the surf and they'd fire rockets at them. For about six weeks they just strafed the beach and fired rockets constantly at the barrels in the surf. The rockets would blow a hole about a metre deep. They weren't explosive, it was just the impact."

"They had so much ammunition that towards the end, they were firing all six at once. And all these things would come shooting down. They almost hit one of the guard shacks with a rocket."

"We would go up and talk with the airforce guys. We could see they were bored in their little guard shacks, chatting away with us. They weren't watching anything hardly at all, because this one kid that was with us, he went off on his own and wandered behind the sand dunes. They used to dump all the shells there and those .50-calibre shells are neat, brass shells, and there were all the clips from the machine guns and things. So he was up there, gathering shells and the planes came again, right over his head. He was in a big basin in the sand dunes and the planes were coming down and all the shells were dropping around him. He was running around, dodging the shells. Then he ran into an abandoned shack in the back of the sand dunes and cowered in there for an hour or so, while they machine-gunned the hell out of the beach."

"It's quite ironic. That was the federal government that did that. Then, in about 1970 they came along and said, 'Oh, you're not to cut any trees or do anything detrimental to the pristine nature of the park.' That, after they bombed and machine-gunned and fired rockets into the beach!"

esterday's News
(from the edge of the world)

"Tofino is the capital of Tofino" from *What We Know So Far*

old headlines
read for the first time
crumpling paper
to fire the wood stove

FAMINE IN AFRICA
still waiting for rain   seed   peace

this last past February a record 787 mm of rain
alder seedlings thick
in the gravel around the house foundation
a prickly lawn for two weeks perhaps a month
the time it takes for seedling to become tree
trees to become forest

WAR AGAINST TERRORISM
and government bills against terrorism
and police action against
and civil disobedience

> ♪*hear it again and again and again*
> *no pasarán Megin River*
> *no pasarán Clayoquot River*
> *no pasarán Flores Island* ♪

tree ring leaders   *everyone in town knows where they live*
count campaigns   dollars of support   *or could look*
voting shares in MacMillan Bloedel   *in the phone book*
                        only the appliance repair man
                            has an unlisted number

     bodies lie on the road / bulldozers and logging trucks stop
fear trees mined with spikes / fear snipers gunning   the engine
and so far
the trucks turn back
the bodies get up and walk away
this coastal village
so far removed from the centre of the world
that it is its own universe
the vortical centre spinning Pacific storms
tides rise and fall around it
one thin line of asphalt and black cable
the umbilical cord

its greatest fears: that the sea will rise up against it
and the earth break like china melt to liquid rock or quicksand
that it will never see the sun

WOMAN STILL MISSING
who disappeared three weeks ago
slipped from a rocky headland into a roiling sea
if it releases its bear embrace and returns her
she will be mauled
faceless   without skin
stumps for legs   a mermaid's tale begun

or they could find her
    eating crab
    in a downtown restaurant
on the other side of the pass

so far away
the news when it filters back
is about
us

each paper ball lobbed into the fire box
comfort
fleeting as the world's attention

Janice Lore

Japanese Glass Balls

"The glass fishing floats from Japan were a dime a dozen on the beach. We had all these glass balls stored in big piles behind the house."

"One day - I forget what year it was - it would have had to be '56, something like that - I came home from work. It was March, I think. And Mum was all excited."

"'Oh there's glass balls everywhere! All over the beach!' she said."

"She'd made little piles of them all around, because they were mostly grapefruit size and some, oh, maybe football size, and orange size. Our neighbour, Paul Norton, came along in his jeep and said, "This is the way to beachcomb. I'll just drive along and you guys throw them in!"

"So we just wandered along, picking them up, one each side of the truck. We had 236 glass balls in a mile and a half of beach, from our beach to Green Point."

"There was sort-of an unwritten code, that from Greenpoint on to Incinerator, was Peggy's turf. Before that there was the Donahues at Lovekin's, so they had from the base of the hill to Schooner Cove. They could do all of Schooner Cove if they wanted, which they did often."

 eading Faces

I arrived at the information meeting on fish farms in Clayoquot Sound just as the first presenter was being introduced. The small room was crowded with observers. If the board members sitting around the huge conference table were disconcerted by the crowd, their impassive faces did not register it. I took the last empty chair.

A young bearded scientist began talking about pollution from fish farms. He spoke of government regulations being too permissive. When he described how only four fish farms put out more sewage than the city of Seattle, I expected the faces to register shock, but they only hardened.

The chairperson, a woman with a frank, welcoming manner, called the next speaker - David. The older,

Native man sitting next to me rose. He had been grunting softly at disturbing facts.

"Come," he motioned to a young Native man, who followed him to the foot of the table and sat down. David, standing, spoke quietly.

"We have been here a long time and we're staying," he said. He laid his hand on the young man's shoulder. "Billy, here, is staying. Scientists come with big words and numbers which prove what we could tell you using only common sense. Put something foreign in the environment and bad things will happen that will affect this young man's life" - again he touched Billy's shoulder - "affect his children and his children's children."

Billy sat mutely, his deeply dimpled face unreadable.

David then spoke of his tribe's haahoolthi, the deep responsibility for the land.

"The sea, the land, the air, the animals, us - all is one," he said. "So we must look after it. We thank the scientists for their facts. They are a good addition to our common sense."

One other scientist, who didn't look like a scientist, spoke so convincingly I was persuaded that fish farms should fold up their netcages and disappear. The stone-faced people will likely do nothing, I thought. But I felt that, someday, David and dimpled Billy would.

Shirley Langer

Japanese Glass Balls

"So we had all these glass balls behind the house and we gave away, oh, gangs and gangs of them, to our guests when we had the Comber's. We thought, 'Oh well, they're endless, they just keep coming in, so, here, you can have one, you can have one - oh! - complimentary glass balls!' Just like the crabs, here at Vargas. Then, all of a sudden they stopped coming in."

"The best one I ever found, somebody stole it out of the pile. I wandered down one night when it was almost dark. I happened to look and there was a big glass ball, one of the larger ones. It was really dark in colour and I thought, 'God Almighty! Can that be one of those famous, royal red ones?' Because everyone was looking for those and some people found them. Peggy had one and the

Donahues had two. So I brought this thing home and it was amber, dark amber, like a beer bottle. I treasured that and I kept it safely in the pile, but some clown came and stole it."

"Apparently, I heard a rumour that the Japanese are starting to use them again because plastic is becoming so expensive in Japan. They might go to the moulded type, though. I found a clear moulded one at Comber's years and years ago. It had some Russian figures on it."

The 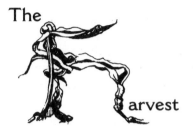arvest

Five a.m. I lift my head, gaze out the window. The mouth of Bamfield Inlet is the window to a dream. Starkly silhouetted shores, bristling with trees, give way to silvery flat calm water and radiant arrival of dawn. Somewhere between house and boat, my desire to be in bed shifts to anticipation of the water. Once again, I become a passenger in the little yellow boat; vessel of many kelp harvests; keeper of safe passage for the harvesters she ferries.

This morning it's a shore harvest, *Laminaria Setchelli*, or kombu, the brownish blades bobbing where low tide meets rocky outcroppings. Captain Kelp, our sage of seaweed, our guru of the gurgling gulches where *Laminaria* dwells, noses his craft up to a rock and we step out onto slippery sea cabbage - *Hedophyllum* - to search out the largest and healthiest of the plants, rubbery and robust, sensual and slippery. I find a spot out of reach of surge and surf and begin my task. I am the surgeon who wields the scalpel, separating blade from stipe. My operating theatre comes complete with urchins, starfish, anemones. Two grey whales sigh, startling me.

As I begin, the view from where I sit, crouch, scramble, is of sea and sky merging into a monochrome pool of shimmering luminescence. Time takes a funny lurching leap, the morning changes and my view becomes one of startlingly bright water, contrasting with surreal blue sky. Soon a forest of little stipes, bladeless until next season's re-growth, a pile of filled sacks and a rising tide signal time for departure. The Kelp Express nudges in and we're away, marine farmers with a bountiful crop.

Heather Cooper

Lumber Spills

"There were several lumber spills. Actually, just before we got to Long Beach the Webbs had built a whole bunch of very rustic cabins from a freighter load of lumber. That was the Wickaninnish Lodge. The Webbs hardly had any money. None of us had any money. And lumber was really hard to come by, other than that there was a mill at MacLean's point."

"Still, whenever there was a deck cargo of lumber lost, it piled up like jack straws all over the beach. And, being as how you could drive on the beach it was a piece of cake. You'd just drive down and throw it on the truck and run back down and grab more. That's when the beach-combing laws - the honour system - went a little bit by the wayside. Because people from Tofino and Ucluelet would come out as well and they didn't know the honour system, they didn't play by the rules."

"You'd have it all piled up nicely, ready to come back for another load and you'd come back and it would be gone! Soon as you made your stack, that was yours," Marilyn explains the honour system further.

"And you'd put a little ribbon on it, or a bottle, or a float, or a glass ball. But people from Tofino or Ucluelet would come driving along and think, "Oh well, this is handy," and ch-ch-ch [throw it on their trucks]."

"So the rules kind-of went by the wayside."

Booty!

I once left the coast for a few years. I often dreamed of the sea and its mysteries. When my family and I returned, it was a time of new beginnings and endless possibilities.

Shortly after our arrival I took my daughter for a walk on Long Beach. It was a magical day of sunshine and warm winds, of squealing at the waves lapping at our rolled-up pants. My daughter was new to the joys of discovering crab shells, bull kelp and Japanese whiskey bottles. We were beachcombers!

As we hiked further the crowds thinned. Periodically, an urban beach marcher would pass us without saying hello. We felt very superior.

During snacky time I spied a large awkward shape in the breakers. I realized I was looking at a container which had fallen off a barge or freighter.

It was coming to shore.
No one else was around -
My God, I was going to be RICH!

Containers are usually full of computers or TV's or cool stereo stuff. Heck, even running shoes for everyone sounded pretty good. Where could I stash the stuff? Who could I call to come?

But -
  a) The door of the container was firmly shut;
  b) I was in a national park whose staff might not respect my ad hoc definition of salvager's rights; and
  c) I had a four-year-old assistant.
Clearly there were hurdles to my dreams of honourable piracy.

Suddenly the container bounced in the surf, hit the beach and - Great Neptune! - the doors flew open towards me. I screamed at my darling to stay put, and, greed coursing through my veins, leaped through the surf. I drew near and spied hundreds of boxes of produce. Oh well, maybe I could be West Coast Mango King for a few days. I ripped open the boxes. . . .

The entire container was full of florist-grade salal en route from Washington State to Japan.

It was a quiet drive home.

Postscript: As my family later searched for a place to live in Tofino, the container started to look pretty good.

Bill Morrison

Lumber Spills

"Dennis Singleton was the school bus driver. One time, before he stopped to pick us up, he'd heard some rumours about lumber floating in on the beach. When we got up and got ready for school, we noticed right away that there was lumber, so we played hooky. Singleton stopped for us and he was mad, shouting out the window: 'Goddamn Buckle boys are getting all the lumber!'

"Well, he wanted some too, so he rushed in and dropped all the kids off and then came rushing back. He stripped down to his shorts and waded in the creek, pulling these six-by-sixes up. They were fir six-by-sixes and there was some planking, going up to two-by-sixteens. Lots of it. It was stacked like jack straws on the beach."

"I don't know how Singleton ever figured he would get it up off the beach. All the accesses were blocked, except ours. And we didn't want to let him use *our* access to go down the beach and pick *our* lumber up!"

"He pulled all these six-by-sixes out of the water - and the creek was thrashing around and the logs were floating and he could have got killed - and then it dawned on him that his work had just begun, because he had to drag it up over the logs and onto the road and load it onto a truck and so on."

"So he said 'Maybe you guys can have this, I can't see how I can deal with this.'"

"'Oh thanks, Dennis,' we said, 'we thought you'd say that!' We used to tease him a lot, riding on the school bus all the time. I think we ended up playing hooky for two or three days in a row and he was pretty mad."

eautiful Dreamer

Fred, you were a man ahead of your time for Tofino!
Granted, your clearcut would have raised a few
eyebrows at today's bakery, but as your castle rose
from the stump field and we watched as you
methodically nailed the rungs up the single remaining
spruce, our panic might have softened to curiosity.

When you first perched on the chair at the top of that
tree, wound up your gramophone and let the music
spill out over Clayoquot Sound, we would have gone
to our front doors, looked towards your "Dream Isle"
with Mount Mariner's glacier shimmering in the

distance and known for sure that another quirky eccentric had arrived at the end of the road and wasn't leaving any time soon.

The princess you painted in the castle tower, the bike path circumnavigating Dream Isle, your eagerness to share your gramophone and new records and, of course, your poetry (*When Noah Entered the Ark*, and others you penned) would have captivated us all. Who could resist a quiet dreamer who never went without a suit jacket and called his niece Cissywiss?

But, of course, you did leave us. In the end Clayoquot Sound claimed you for good before you could win over Alma or Olive or Winnie (or was it Ethel? It's so hard to know who to believe) with your cornet serenades, poems and unassuming ways. I like to think that instead of that frantic, numbing swim from Mission Point to the spit on Clayoquot Island, when you first swam for your skiff and then swam for your life, instead of all that, you had a more peaceful leaving. I want to believe that drowning is as serene as people say and that instead of a marathon swim, you silently slipped below the surface and effortlessly shifted from breathing the air of Clayoquot Sound to breathing the water. I

want to think that you gazed at Lone Cone through garlands of
kelp stretching out above you like streamers, prayed to your God,
and hummed one of your favourites - *A Perfect Day*.

Adrienne Mason

** Fred Tibbs arrived on the west coast in 1908 and
first pre-empted land near Long Beach. Not long
after, he bought an island off Tofino and named it
Dream Isle. Over time Tibbs became well known
for his colourful behaviour. He died of exhaustion
after pursuing his skiff, The Agnes, which drifted
away while he was tending the harbour lights off
Mission Point. Some accounts say that he finished
his work, then carefully removed and hung up his
clothes before plunging in after his drifting boat.
He never reached it and collapsed, then died on
Clayoquot Island.*

The Shake Block Spill

"There was a shake block barge that went down a few years ago. I actually saw the barge go by here and it looked quite low in the water. There was a little swell rolling in and the swell seemed to be breaking level with the deck. It had been loading at various places along the coast, coming from Nootka Island. I think it had come down the inside to avoid the big swell on the outside."

"I remember saying, 'Wouldn't it be neat if that thing sunk and all the blocks floated over here?'

"My son, Brian, phoned me up the morning after the barge had gone by and said, 'Did you hear about the shake block spill?' and I said, 'What? That barge that went by here? I *wished* it to sink!'

"Neil said, 'Wouldn't that be nice if it sunk?' Because it looked a little askew," Marilyn adds.

"I guess it was getting near Christmas and the

guys who were towing it were antsy to get back to town for Christmas and all that sort of thing. They were towing away, not paying attention to the thing. Then, off Long Beach, they looked back and there was just the bow of it sticking up. They don't know how long it had been under for. There was a huge front-end loader, a $250,000 machine and now it's down on the bottom off Long Beach. They had a pick-up truck there too. So there's another vehicle sunk off Long Beach."

"But the blocks floated. . . ."

 ith Any Luck

All of us go out in grace
Death has a way of resolving life
Like an old boat too full of history
will be forgiven on the bottom
we sink like stones in our reality
but never quite touch ground

I have no theories for you
but this: It's either raining
or a bear is pissing on the porch
If a westerly is blowing today
the fog might burn off
but it might not
If the moon rises before the sun
the fish will be here by noon Monday
Otherwise if the westerly switches to north
and the eagles divebomb the tide
the fog will give up its captured dreamers
leaving us all to hold the stern line
witness to another great escape

deborah vansickle

Contributing Authors

Joanne Bealy is a freelance writer living on Salt Spring Island. Her essays and poetry have appeared in various journals.

Heather Cooper lives in Bamfield with her husband. She is a fibre artist and part-time kelp harvester who was born in Saskatchewan and raised her three children in the mountains. She feels very lucky to have finally landed by the sea for inspiration for her art and writing.

Louis Druehl is professor emeritus of marine botany, Simon Fraser University. He lives in Bamfield, BC, with his spouse Rae Hopkins, where he works at the Bamfield Marine Station and on their kelp farm. His other publications are in scientific journals and he is the author of *Pacific Seaweeds*.

Frank Harper is a writer of fiction, journalism and plays who has lived in Clayoquot Sound for 31 years. He has caught one fish, a spring salmon. He caught it for his ancient angel mother who was visiting from the city.

Sylvia Harron put down roots in a few places before she arrived on the West Coast four years ago. Although she still hungers occasionally for a clear prairie sky or the warmth of a trade wind, for the first time in her life, she has no plans to go anywhere.

Betty Krawczyk is a Raging Granny, best known for the year she spent in jail recently, after blockading the Elaho Valley. She is the author of *Clayoquot, The Sound Of My Heart* and her latest book, *Lock Me Up Or Let Me Go*.

Mike Laanela grew up on Vancouver Island. He worked as a journalist in Australia for several years, before returning to complete his Masters in journalism at U.B.C.

Dan Lewis has paddled on the west coast since 1978 and lived in Tofino since 1991 where he teaches kayaking.

Shirley Langer arrived on the west coast in 1995. One of her *Amazing But True Tales From Tofino*, has been published in the anthology, *Messages From La La Land*. A founding member of the Clayoquot Writers' Group, Shirley is currently researching a book on literacy in Cuba.

Janice Lore has lived in Tofino BC since 1994. Her work has appeared in literary magazines across the country, and on CBC and CHOO FM radio. Her first chapbook, *Ipsissima Verba*, a long poem, will be published in the Spring, 2003.

Christine Lowther is the author of *A Cabin in Clayoquot* and *New Power* and is a freelance writer. She is currently at work on a book about floathouse life.

Born and raised in Victoria, **Janis McDougall** has lived in Tofino since 1978. Poetry provides a creative outlet in her eventful life as mother of Lia and assistant to students with special needs.

Adrienne Mason is a writer, biologist and life-long resident of Vancouver Island. She gets inspiration from exploring the coastal environment with her husband and two daughters. Adrienne lives in Tofino, where she writes books and articles for adults and children, as well as educational and technical papers.

Bill Morrison learned to type in central Canada but didn't have much to say until he arrived on Vancouver Island. He's worked as a biologist, fisherman and teacher. His family sometimes wonders if the fish preoccupation is going to wear off soon.

Karen Odenwald keeps busy as a technical writer, editor and graphic designer. She developed her passion for writing from several challenging cycling trips and expensive language courses in Europe. She currently calls Bamfield and the rugged west coast home.

deb vansickle lives in Ucluelet and has worked in the fishing industry for many years. She is currently working on a collection of poems *With Any Luck*.

Jacqueline Windh roamed the world for a decade and a half before settling on Vancouver Island's west coast. She lives in Tofino, where she works as wilderness guide, photographer and writer. She is a devoted mother to Kermit, Stripe and Little Runt.